From the *Animated Hero Classics*™

Helen Keller

Total Learning Resource and Activity Book

By:
M. G. Ron Johnson,
Tony Salerno, and Katherine Vawter

TEACHER GUIDE

This Total Learning Resource and Activity Book is used to supplement the "Helen Keller" video from the *Animated Hero Classics*™ series from Nest Entertainment, Inc.

The purpose of this book is to help elementary age students learn and retain the story of "Helen Keller" in a fun, yet educational way. The activities are designed to integrate the video across the curriculum and may be completed individually or with the whole class. There are questions and group activities at the end.

Although most of the answers to each activity can be found by watching the "Helen Keller" video, there are activities that give additional facts about Helen Keller's life. There is an answer key in the back of the book for your convenience.

Nest Entertainment, Inc. hopes that this activity book will make your investment in the *Animated Hero Classics*™ even more valuable as you use it to help your students develop a greater love for history and learning.

LEVEL OF DIFFICULTY

The activities in this book are not restricted to any one grade level. They are designed for three levels of difficulty from the perspective of eight to ten-year-olds. An activity rated at one symbol will be easy for this age group. A two-symbol activity will match their achievement level while they will find the three-symbol activity more difficult.

easy   intermediate   difficult

CURRICULUM RELATED

These educational activities are related interdisciplinarily to social studies (geography, history, culture), language arts (spelling, creative writing, grammar, literature), math (simple equations), and science. There are also activities for character development, video awareness, problem solving, music, and art. The subject codes below are for your convenience.

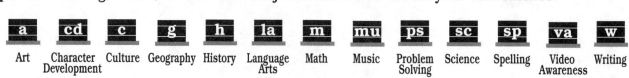

a	cd	c	g	h	la	m	mu	ps	sc	sp	va	w
Art	Character Development	Culture	Geography	History	Language Arts	Math	Music	Problem Solving	Science	Spelling	Video Awareness	Writing

TABLE
OF CONTENTS

REFERENCES
for your convenience

For those wishing to further study the life of Helen Keller, some of the references used in research for the Total Learning Resource and Activity Book are listed below, along with other titles that may be of interest.

Adler, David A., *A Picture Book of Helen Keller*, Holiday House, New York, 1990.

Birch, Beverley, *Louis Braille*, Gareth Stevens Children's Books, Milwaukee, 1989.

Brooks, Van Wyck, *Helen Keller, Sketch for a Portrait*, E. P. Dutton & Co., Inc., New York, 1956.

Davidson, Margaret, *Louis Braille, the Boy Who Invented Books for the Blind*, Scholastic Book Services, New York, 1971.

DeGering, Etta, *Seeing Fingers, The Story of Louis Braille*, David McKay Company, Inc., New York, 1962.

Hickok, Lorena, *The Story of Helen Keller*, Grosset & Dunlap, New York, 1958.

Johnson, Ann Donegan, *The Value of Determination, The Story of Helen Keller*, Value Communications, Inc., La Jolla, California, 1976.

Keller, Helen, *The Story of My Life*, Doubleday & Company, Inc., Garden City, New York, 1905.

Kudlinski, Kathleen V., *Helen Keller, A Light for the Blind*, Viking Kestrel, New York, 1989

Lash, Joseph P., *Helen and Teacher, The Story of Helen Keller and Anne Sullivan Macy*, Delacorte Press/Seymour Lawrence, New York, 1980.

Peare, Catherine Owens, *The Helen Keller Story*, Thomas Y. Crowell, New York, 1959.

Sabin, Francene, *The Courage of Helen Keller*, Troll Associates, Mahwah, New Jersey, 1982.

Wayne, Bennett, *Four Women of Courage*, Garrard Publishing Company, Champaign, Illinois, 1975.

Wepman, Dennis, *Helen Keller, American Women of Achievement*, Chelsea House Publishers, New York, 1987.

Nest Entertainment, Inc. would like to thank the Helen Keller National Center for Deaf-Blind Youths and Adults for their assistance on this project.

**Helen Keller is able to see
and hear when she is born.**

Using Your Sense

We have five senses. They are hearing, seeing, smelling, tasting and touching. We use some of our senses in almost everything we do.

Look at each picture. Circle the sense or senses that you think is used to learn about it. Write the number of senses that may be used in the box.

	HEAR SEE SMELL TASTE TOUCH		HEAR SEE SMELL TASTE TOUCH		HEAR SEE SMELL TASTE TOUCH
	HEAR SEE SMELL TASTE TOUCH		HEAR SEE SMELL TASTE TOUCH	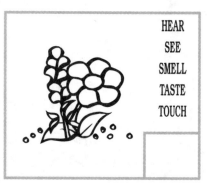	HEAR SEE SMELL TASTE TOUCH
	HEAR SEE SMELL TASTE TOUCH		HEAR SEE SMELL TASTE TOUCH		HEAR SEE SMELL TASTE TOUCH

How many times did you use each of the senses?

Hearing____   Seeing____   Smelling____   Tasting____   Touching____

SHAPE THE ANSWER

Helen received love from her mother and father, but there is one thing she did not receive. Find what she needed, but did not receive. The shapes below have the answer.

Match the shapes above the lines with the shapes in the Code Box. Write the correct letter on the line.

CODE BOX

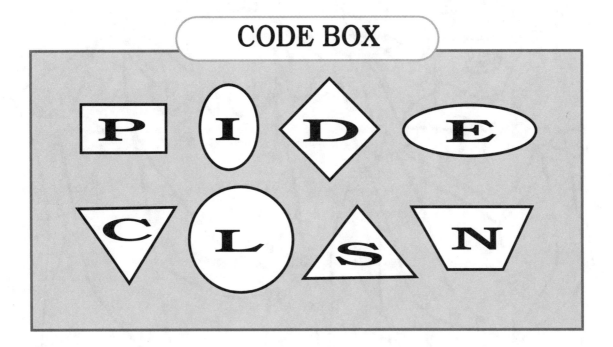

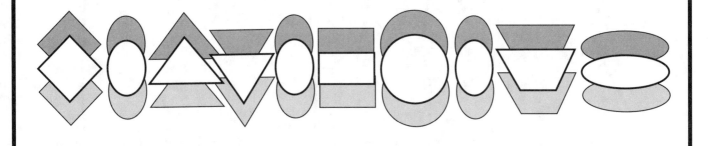

_____

cd h la ps sp

"Mr. & Mrs. Keller, I'm sorry to tell you that Helen is blind and deaf."

MAKE A MOTION

Before Helen had a teacher, she made signs and motions to communicate. Match the motions with the picture of what or who Helen wanted.

Motions when made:

1. Pretending to put glasses on.

2. Cutting or slicing and spreading.

3. Sucking her fingers.

4. Turning a handle and shivering.

5. Pulling her hair into a knot on the back of her head.

6. Putting her hands to her mouth and moving lips.

What Helen wanted:

Food or candy

Helen's mother

Bread and butter

Helen's father

Helen's baby sister

Ice cream

The 5 Senses

Smelling   Tasting   Touching

Hearing   Seeing

Which of the five senses will help you to do this? Look at the picture. Write the number of the sense that you think is needed in the box. There may be more than one of the senses used.

HEARING = 1   SEEING = 2   SMELLING = 3   TASTING = 4   TOUCHING = 5

Helen becomes angry when Mrs. Keller does not understand her.

HELEN'S AMAZING ANAGRAMS

An anagram is a word you make by rearranging the letters in another word. Rearrange the words at the beginning of each sentence to form a new word that will complete the sentence. Copy your new word on the blank.

1 hare   When Helen was born she was able to see and _____.

2 rangy   Helen became _____ when no one understood her.

3 whit   Helen's mother needed help _____ her.

4 nest   Her mother _____ for someone to help.

5 mace   Anne Sullivan _____ to teach Helen.

6 charm   It was in the month of _____ that Anne arrived.

7 smite   Anne tried many _____ to teach Helen how to eat with a spoon.

8 detest   Helen _____ Anne's patience many times.

9 tops   Anne would never _____ trying to teach Helen.

10 bale   Helen became _____ to read, write, and communicate with others.

Keller's Crossword

ACROSS

1. The sense of the tongue.
4. Organ of hearing.
5. Unable to hear.
8. A scent.
10. Anne Sullivan's pupil.
11. Unable to see.
13. The first thing Helen understood the name for.
15. Using the hand signs to communicate to a deaf person.
16. Anne wrote signs in Helen's _____.

DOWN

2. Helen's teacher (full name).
3. Organ of sight.
6. Another word for touch.
7. The sense through the nose.
9. Anne first taught Helen to _____.
10. The sense through the ears.
12. Anne's nationality.
14. The sense through the eyes.

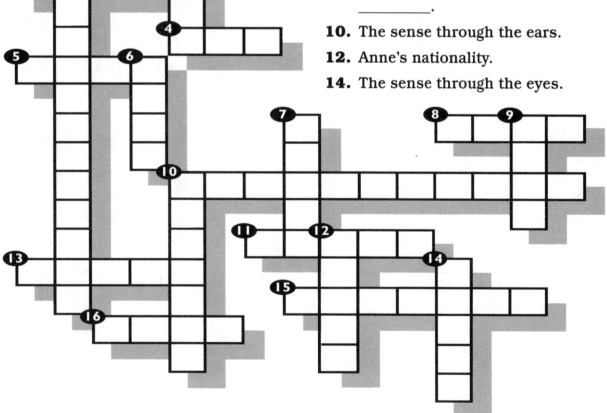

ALPHABET MAZE

What was Helen Keller like when Anne Sullivan first met her?

Go through the maze below and circle every other letter, starting with the S. The circled letters spell the answer. Write the letters on the spaces below to complete the sentence.

Begin Here

S	E	H	A	A	E	W	A	I	D	I	C	M
A	H	T	F	T	A	L	E	R	M	O	I	E
S	G	E	E	E	B	K	M	L	Z	N	B	A
E	E	G	D	K	I	F	K	S	L	S	M	M
A	R	W	H	A	T	I	C	D	I	A	X	L
U	W	O	S	P	L	L	I	E	K	A	L	M
S	R	A	I	S	I	L	N	A	R	N	S	I

End Here

Anne Sullivan said, " __ __ __ __   __ __ __ __ __   __ __ __

__ __   __ __ __ __ __   __ __ __ __ __ __ *!"*

© 1996, Nest Entertainment, Inc. • 6100 Colwell Blvd., Irving, TX 75039

14

Mr. Anagnos tells Anne Sullivan about Helen.

LEARN BY TOUCH

A person who is deaf-blind may be able to touch and feel to learn what objects are. Color the things that you think a deaf-blind person may be able to learn what it is by feeling.

Banana

Leaf

Orange

Kitten

Apple

Brush

Bar of Soap

Ball

Egg

Flower

LEARN BY SMELL

Color the things that you think a deaf-blind person may be able to smell and learn what it is.

Banana

Glass of Water

Orange

Egg

Bar of Soap

Ice Cream Cone

Lemon

Cup of Coffee

Flower

Leaf

Ball

SC

DM WORD X SEARCH GH

Find and circle the words in the puzzle. The words are listed below the puzzle in the Word Box. They may be forward, backward, up, down, or diagonal.

```
S  T  W  A  T  E  R  A  S  S  D  O  M  H  T
C  L  O  C  O  M  M  U  N  I  C  A  T  E  N
H  A  S  P  E  L  L  B  S  G  E  N  A  L  R
M  R  I  S  N  L  E  C  O  N  A  C  S  E  E
T  W  A  N  I  S  I  P  R  E  H  O  P  N  A
L  R  N  V  C  P  E  K  D  E  A  F  A  C  B
N  A  A  S  L  C  P  E  R  D  L  G  H  R  P
A  N  B  I  C  E  B  L  A  N  G  U  A  G  E
D  N  N  E  D  O  L  L  F  H  K  A  N  P  B
R  E  S  A  T  B  V  E  I  W  Y  Z  D  A  P
L  U  N  R  H  E  A  R  A  N  B  E  G  F  H
K  M  O  S  L  Y  N  W  O  R  D  S  P  R  S
T  V  L  A  U  R  A  B  R  I  D  G  M  A  N
```

___ Anne	___ doll	___ language	___ spell
___ blind	___ hand	___ Laura Bridgman	___ Sullivan
___ communicate	___ hear	___ obey	___ teacher
___ deaf	___ Helen	___ see	___ water
___ discipline	___ Keller	___ sign	___ words

Anne Sullivan meets Helen Keller.

Braille's Brilliant Idea

Helen Keller learned to read by using a system of printing for the blind called Braille. This system was named after the inventor Louis Braille from France. Louis was only fourteen years old when he started working on a system of reading. He stuck pins in a piece of paper to make the raised dots.

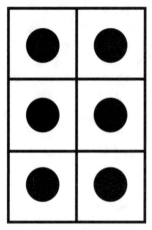

Braille uses a combination of raised dots to represent the letters of the alphabet. The reader "reads" with his fingers, touching the letters to identify each one.

The first ten letters of the alphabet (a-j) uses the top two rows of dots. The next ten letters (k-t) uses the top two rows plus one dot from the third row. The last six letters (u-z) uses all the dots, except for "w", which is a reversed "r". (The Braille alphabet is shown on page 21.)

Try making your own Braille system. Draw your series of dots in the box below. Then make up a combination of dots for each letter of the alphabet. Give the code to your friends and send them a message.

A =	E =	I =	M =	Q =	U =	Y =
B =	F =	J =	N =	R =	V =	Z =
C =	G =	K =	O =	S =	W =	
D =	H =	L =	P =	T =	X =	

BRAILLE CODE FUN

BRAILLE CODE FUN

Decode the word below by using the Braille system of dots. Match the combination of dots above the blanks with the dots in the Braille Code Box and write the correct letter on the blank.

These dots are not raised as they would be in a Braille book, but they are in the same position.

You will discover the word that is a character quality that Helen Keller had. This word helped her to accomplish things that people thought were impossible for a deaf-blind person.

Braille Code Box

A	B	C	D
E	F	G	H
I	J	K	L
M	N	O	P
Q	R	S	T
U	V	W	X
Y	Z		
and	for	of	the

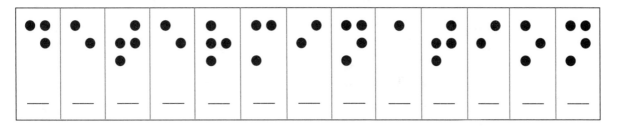

Try writing your name in Braille! _____

Fun with Math and Words

Anne Sullivan believed that a certain behavior must be learned before Helen could be taught language. To find what the behavior was, work the problems and write the letters on the blanks.

LETTER/NUMBER CODE BOX

A = 3	C = 5	O = 8	Y = 10
B = 4	E = 6	T = 9	N = 7

$$\begin{array}{c} 4 \\ +5 \\ \hline \end{array} \qquad \begin{array}{c} 5 \\ +3 \\ \hline \end{array} \qquad \begin{array}{c} 4 \\ +4 \\ \hline \end{array} \qquad \begin{array}{c} 2 \\ +2 \\ \hline \end{array} \qquad \begin{array}{c} 4 \\ +2 \\ \hline \end{array} \qquad \begin{array}{c} 7 \\ +3 \\ \hline \end{array}$$

⬜ ⬜   ⬜ ⬜ ⬜ ⬜

___ ___ ___ ___ ___ ___

$$\begin{array}{c} 2 \\ +1 \\ \hline \end{array} \qquad \begin{array}{c} 3 \\ +4 \\ \hline \end{array} \qquad \begin{array}{c} 5 \\ +2 \\ \hline \end{array} \qquad \begin{array}{c} 3 \\ +3 \\ \hline \end{array}$$

⬜ ⬜ ⬜ ⬜

___ ___ ___ ___

What must Helen learn?

___ ___ ___ ___ ___ ___ ___ ___ ___ ___ ___.

© 1996, Nest Entertainment, Inc. • 6100 Colwell Blvd., Irving, TX 75039

Anne is surprised to see Helen eating from her father's plate.

FIND THE WORDS

Helen's father did not believe Anne could teach Helen to obey or to spell words. Why was she successful? Color the puzzle as directed. Then copy the uncolored letters, in order, on the lines below.

Color the spaces: **B** = blue   **Y** = yellow   **R** = red

B	Y	B	S	R	R	R	H	Y	R	Y	Y	E	R	Y	R
Y	H	Y	R	R	Y	Y	Y	R	Y	R	B	B	Y	R	Y
B	Y	B	Y	Y	A	B	B	Y	R	Y	Y	Y	R	D	R
R	R	R	Y	Y	Y	Y	Y	R	R	R	R	B	B	B	B
B	B	B	P	Y	Y	B	R	B	A	B	R	B	Y	R	R
Y	Y	Y	Y	Y	Y	R	B	R	Y	R	B	R	Y	B	B
R	B	R	Y	R	T	B	R	B	Y	B	R	B	I	Y	Y
B	R	B	E	R	Y	Y	Y	N	Y	Y	Y	Y	Y	B	B
R	B	R	B	Y	C	R	R	R	B	B	B	B	E	Y	Y

__ __ __   __ __ __

__ __ __ __ __ __ __ __ __ __'

PICTURE SEQUENCE

Look at each picture below. Read the words below the picture. Number each picture in the order it happened.

Anne Sullivan meets Helen Keller.

———

Helen cannot hear or see.

———

Helen loves to chase butterflies.

———

Helen learns to finger-spell.

———

Helen learns to eat with a spoon.

———

Mr. and Mrs. Keller learn that their daughter is deaf and blind.

———

Helen does not like for her hair to be brushed!

SIGN THE ANSWER

Helen Keller became friends with a very famous author. Discover who this author is by solving the code below.

Use the one hand manual alphabet symbols to help you decode the words. Match the hand signs below with the signs in the Code Box. Write the correct letter in the box.

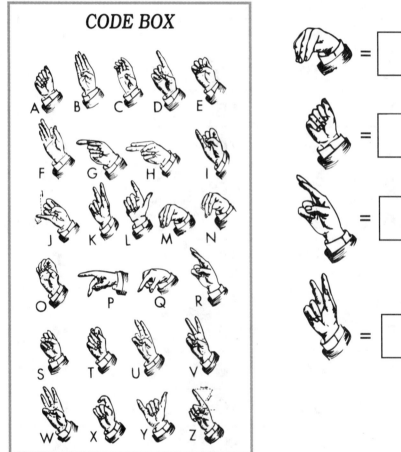

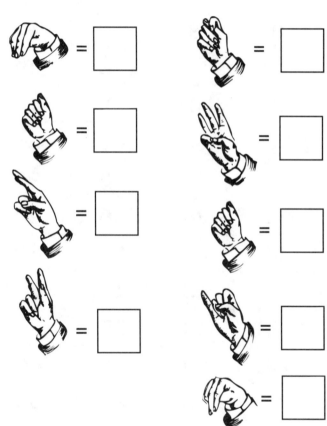

BONUS QUESTION! CAN YOU NAME ONE OF THE BOOKS THIS FAMOUS AUTHOR WROTE?

_____

Try signing your own name!

NUMBER SEQUENCE

Helen never called Anne Sullivan by her name. Solve the puzzle below to find the name that Helen called Anne for the rest of her life.

Step One: Circle the letter at the end of the row if the numerals are multiples of five.

6	8	10	12	14	16	**S**
10	15	20	25	30	35	**C**
3	6	9	12	15	18	**O**
50	55	60	65	70	75	**H**
75	80	85	90	95	100	**A**
22	24	26	28	30	32	**R**
25	30	35	40	45	50	**T**
8	12	16	20	24	28	**B**
5	10	15	20	25	30	**E**
10	20	30	40	50	60	**T**
20	25	30	35	40	45	**E**
65	70	75	80	85	90	**R**

Step Two: Unscramble the circled letters to form the name that Helen called Anne. Write the letters on the spaces below.

____ ____ ____ ____ ____ ____

© 1996, Nest Entertainment, Inc. • 6100 Colwell Blvd., Irving, TX 75039

The simple block letters of the alphabet below can be used to communicate with most deaf-blind persons. Look at the lines, arrows, and numbers that show the proper direction to form the letters.

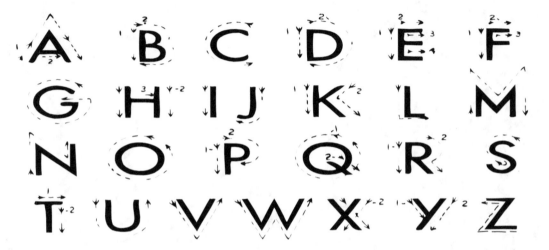

Practice drawing the letters in your own hand. Print only in the palm area. Do not try to connect letters.

Try printing words in your friends' hands to see if they can guess what you are saying. Have them print words in your hand. Do not look at your hand while they are writing!

Words that I guessed correctly:	Words that a friend guessed correctly:
_____ _____	_____ _____
_____ _____	_____ _____
_____ _____	_____ _____
_____ _____	_____ _____
_____ _____	_____ _____

Anne Sullivan finally calms her wild student with love and discipline.

MIX 'N' MATCH CODE

Helen Keller wrote a book about her life titled, "The Story of My Life." In it she described how she felt when she first understood the words spelled into her hand.

To find what she wrote, decode the message below. Match the code letter below each blank with the letter in the top row of the Code Box. Copy the letter from the second row on the blank.

CODE BOX

A	B	C	D	E	F	G	H	I	J	K	L	M	N	O	P	Q	R	S	T	U	V	W	X	Y	Z
Z	Y	X	W	V	U	T	S	R	Q	P	O	N	M	L	K	J	I	H	G	F	E	D	C	B	A

Helen Keller wrote:

" __ __   __ __ __ __ __
  N B   S V Z I G

__ __ __ __ __   __ __   __ __ __ __ !"
Y V T Z M   G L   H R M T

h   1a   ps   va

FOLLOW THE LINES

What was Helen doing when Anne was able to teach her what a word meant? Follow the lines to the letters. Write that letter on the blank above the number.

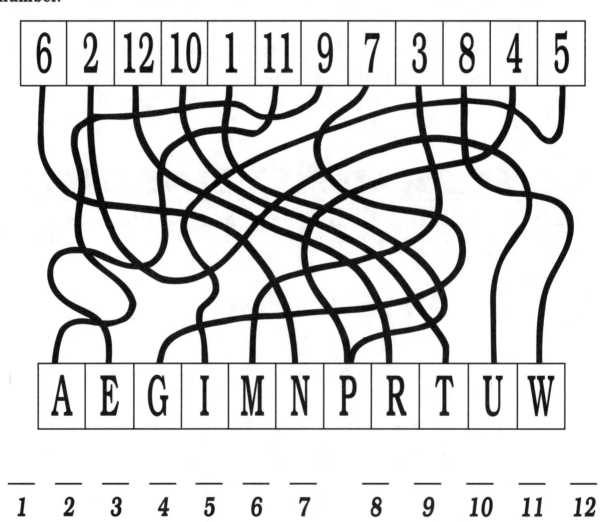

| 6 | 2 | 12 | 10 | 1 | 11 | 9 | 7 | 3 | 8 | 4 | 5 |

| A | E | G | I | M | N | P | R | T | U | W |

__ __ __ __ __ __ __ __ __ __ __ __
1   2   3   4   5   6   7   8   9   10   11   12

What was the first word Helen learned?

__ __ __ __ __
8   9   10   11   12

IN SHAPE WITH HISTORY

Mr. Keller did not like for Anne Sullivan to discipline Helen. He did not understand that discipline was needed before Helen could learn. Solve the puzzle below to find what he said to Anne. Follow the instructions to fill each blank with the correct word.

you   are   Sullivan

fired   Miss

1. Find the word that is in the △ only. Write the word in blank 3.

2. Find the word that is in the ◯ only. Write the word in blank 2.

3. Find the word that is in the ▭ only. Write the word in blank 5.

4. Find the word that is in the △ and ◯ only. Write the word in blank 4.

5. Find the word that is in the ▭ and ◯ only. Write the word in blank 1.

What did Mr. Keller say to Anne Sullivan?

" _____ _____, _____ _____ _____! "
    1   2   3   4   5

"Arthur, we have to give Anne a chance!"

MYSTERY WORDS

Helen's parents took her to see a man who was very interested in educating the deaf. In fact, this man was so interested that he invented the telephone.

Find the name of this famous inventor. Read the questions below and write the answers on the spaces. If you need help, the answers are in the Word Box. Copy all of the circled letters and then unscramble them to find the name of this man.

WORD BOX

Alabama   Anne Sullivan   Civil War   Doll   Fever   Hand   Laura Bridgman   Six

1. In what war did Helen's father fight?

— — — — ◯   — ◯ ◯

2. In what state was Helen born?

◯ — — ◯ ◯ — —

3. Who was Helen's teacher?

◯ — — ◯   — — — ◯ — — — —

4. What was the name of another deaf-blind person who learned to communicate?

— — — ◯ —   — — — ◯ ◯ ◯ — ◯

5. Where would Anne spell words for Helen?

◯ — — —

6. What caused Helen to become deaf and blind?

— ◯ — ◯ —

7. What was the first word spelled into Helen's hand?

— — — ◯

8. How old was Helen when she met this famous inventor?

— — ◯

Copy the circled letters: _____

Unscramble the letters and write the name on the blanks below.

— — — — — — — — —   — — — — — —   — — —

© 1996, Nest Entertainment, Inc. • 6100 Colwell Blvd., Irving, TX 75039

FILL in the BLANK

Learn more about Helen Keller by filling in the blanks with the correct words from the Word Box below.

WORD BOX			
Alabama	book	learn	thirty
Anne	college	signs	two
Sullivan	famous	sister	words
alone	hands	spoon	yes

1. Helen Keller lived in the state of _____.

2. Helen's teacher was _____ _____.

3. Helen had a baby _____.

4. Anne believed Helen could _____.

5. She taught Helen to eat with a _____.

6. She thought Helen would learn faster if they lived _____.

7. Anne asked to be allowed to try it for _____ weeks.

8. When Anne held Helen's hand against her face and nodded, it was telling her "_____".

9. Anne taught Helen the names of many things by making _____ in Helen's _____.

10. Helen learned quickly to spell _____.

11. On the first day Helen learned how to spell words, she learned _____ new words.

12. When Helen was twenty, she went to _____.

13. While in college, Helen wrote a _____ about her life.

14. Helen became a very _____ person.

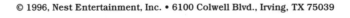

Letter SHUFFLE !

See how many words YOU can make out of the letters in the word:

COMMUNICATE

NOTE: You cannot use any letter more times than it appears in the name.
(For example: no more than one O, two M's, etc.)

2 Letter Words - 1 point each

___ words x 1 = ___ points

3 Letter Words - 2 points each

___ words x 2 = ___ points

4 Letter Words - 3 points each

___ words x 3 = ___ points

5 or More Letter Words - 4 points each

___ words x 4 = ___ points

TOTAL POINTS____:

5-15 = Junior • 16-30 = Intermediate • 31-45 = Advanced • 46-60 points = Ace
61-85 = Champ • 86-100 = Super Champ • 101 and up = Out of Sight!

1a sp

MATCHING  GAME

Match each description on the left with the correct person or item on the right. Write the letters of the correct answers in the boxes.

1. The mother of Helen Keller. ☐

2. A method of communication. ☐

3. A school that Anne Sullivan attended. ☐

4. The teacher of Helen Keller. ☐

5. Helen attended this school at age twenty. ☐

6. A deaf-blind person who taught Anne. ☐

7. The first word that Helen understood. ☐

8. The director of Perkins Institution. ☐

9. A captain in the Confederate army. ☐

10. A deaf-blind person who inspired people around the world. ☐

A. Anne Sullivan

B. Laura Bridgman

C. Helen Keller

D. Michael Anagnos

E. Arthur Keller

F. Finger spelling

G. Kate Keller

H. Perkins Institution for the Blind

I. Water

J. Radcliffe College

TRUE OR FALSE

Read each statement below. If it is true, circle the "T." If it is false, circle the "F."

1. The Keller family lived in Alabama.   T   F

2. Helen Keller was blind and deaf when she was born.   T   F

3. Helen's parents loved her.   T   F

4. Her father was a Confederate soldier in the Civil War.   T   F

5. Helen's parents believed there was no help for her.   T   F

6. They made Helen obey.   T   F

7. The Kellers heard about another blind and deaf girl who learned to communicate.   T   F

8. Anne Sullivan was asked to teach Helen.   T   F

9. Anne did not want to teach Helen.   T   F

10. Helen had very bad manners.   T   F

11. Anne believed Helen must first learn to obey.   T   F

12. The Kellers would not let Anne try.   T   F

13. Anne began spelling names of things in Helen's hand.   T   F

14. Helen was very slow in learning.   T   F

15. Anne and Helen became known all over the world.   T   F

h   va

Helen finally learns to read, write, and communicate with others.

HELEN KELLER
QUESTIONS

1. When did Helen Keller become deaf and blind?

2. What made Helen deaf and blind?

3. How did Helen communicate with her family before she learned the finger alphabet?

4. How did Helen's father treat her?

5. How did Helen act as she grew older?

6. Where did Mr. and Mrs. Keller go to get help for Helen?

7. Who was sent to become Helen's teacher?

8. What was the first word that Anne Sullivan spelled into Helen's hand?

9. What did Anne Sullivan have to do before she could teach Helen?

10. How did Helen's eating habits change after Anne arrived?

11. Did Helen understand the words when she first learned the finger alphabet?

12. What was the first word that Helen understood to be the same as the one Anne was spelling in her hand?

13. What were some things that Helen Keller accomplished?

GUIDELINES FOR HELPING DEAF-BLIND PERSONS

1. When you approach a deaf-blind person, let him know - by a simple touch - that you are near.

2. Make positive but gentle use of any means of communication you adopt.

3. Work out with him a simple but special signal for identifying yourself to him.

4. Learn and use whatever method of communication he knows, however elementary. If a more adequate method might be valuable to him, help him learn it.

5. Always be sure the deaf-blind person understands you, and be sure that you understand him.

6. Encourage him to use his voice if he has speech, even if he knows only a few words.

7. If there are others present, let him know when it is appropriate for him to speak.

8. Always inform him of his whereabouts.

9. Always tell him when you are leaving, even if it is only for a brief period. See that he is comfortably and safely situated. If he is not sitting, he will need something substantial to touch in your absence. Place his hand on it before leaving. Never abandon a deaf-blind person in unfamiliar surroundings.

10. When with a deaf-blind person, keep sufficiently close so that, by physical contact, he will know you are there.

11. In walking, let him take your arm. Never push him ahead of you.

12. Make use of a simple set of signals to let him know when he is about to ascend or descend a flight of stairs, walk through a doorway, board a vehicle. A deaf-blind person holding your arm can usually sense any change in pace or direction.

13. Rely on your natural courtesy, consideration, and common sense. Occasional difficulties in communication are only to be expected.

Reprinted courtesy of Helen Keller National Center for Deaf-Blind Youths and Adults.

THINGS TO THINK ABOUT & DO

NOTE TO THE TEACHER: These are activities for a group to discuss and think about.

THINGS TO THINK ABOUT . . .

1.   Helen Keller was born with sight and hearing, but a high fever left her deaf and blind. She was a very bright, intelligent child. How do you think she must have felt when suddenly she could not see or communicate with anyone?

2.   Why was Mr. Keller's lack of discipline actually harmful for Helen? Why was Anne Sullivan so successful in teaching Helen?

THINGS TO DO . . .

3.   Purchase some sleep shades and industrial ear plugs. While someone is wearing the shades and the ear plugs, have someone else lead him around. Have the person try to take a drink of water. Take the person outside. Have him feel something. Can he identify the object? Invent your own methods of communicating. Try spelling words into the hands. Take turns leading each other around.

4.   Plan a deaf-blind meal. Some of the group may be the helpers, and the rest wear sleep shades and ear plugs. The helpers should set up the food on the table and then guide the others to their chairs. All conversation should cease as soon as they enter the room. No one knows who they are sitting beside. The food can be simple things to eat with the fingers, such as sandwiches. Condiments such as mayonaise, mustard, and peanut butter should be placed on the table for the deaf-blind to use. Be prepared for interesting combinations! Have the diners try pouring from a pitcher. Try to communicate in some way without being able to speak, hear, or see. Mealtime is such a social time for most people that this activity will be difficult to do.

ANSWER
KEY

USING YOUR SENSE — PAGE 6

Answers may vary.

SHAPE THE ANSWER — PAGE 7

D I S C I P L I N E

MAKE A MOTION — PAGE 9

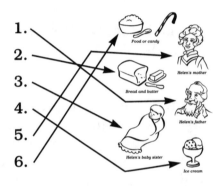

THE FIVE SENSES — PAGE 10

2	4	5
3	2	1

HELEN'S AMAZING ANAGRAMS — PAGE 12

1. hear
2. angry
3. with
4. sent
5. came
6. March
7. times
8. tested
9. stop
10. able

KELLER'S CROSSWORD — PAGE 13

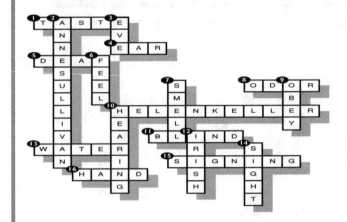

ALPHABET MAZE — PAGE 14

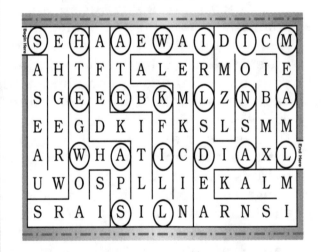

*Anne Sullivan said,
"She was like a wild animal!"*

LEARN BY TOUCH — PAGE 16

Answers may vary.

LEARN BY SMELL — PAGE 17

Answers may vary.

44

WORD SEARCH — PAGE 18

```
S T W A T E R A S S D O M H T
C L O C O M M U N I C A T E N
H A S P E L L B S G E N A L R
M R I S N L E C O N A C S E E
T W A N I S I P R E H O P N A
L R N V C P E K D E A F A C B
N A A S L C P E R D L G H R P
A N B I C E B L A N G U A G E
D N E D O L L F H K A N P B
R E S A T B V E I W Y Z D A P
L U N R H E A R A N B E G F H
K M O S L Y N W O R D S P R S
T V L A U R A B R I D G M A N
```

BRAILLE CODE FUN — PAGE 21

D E T E R M I N A T I O N

FUN WITH MATH AND WORDS
— PAGE 22

9 8   8 4 6 10
3 7 7 6

T O O B E Y
A N N E

FIND THE WORDS — PAGE 24

```
B Y B S R R R H Y R Y Y E R Y R
Y H Y R R Y Y Y R Y R B B Y R Y
B Y B Y Y A B B Y R Y Y Y R D R
R R R Y Y Y Y Y Y R R R B R Y R
B B B P Y Y Y B R B A B R B Y R R
Y Y Y Y Y Y Y R B Y R B R Y B B
R B R Y R T B R B Y B R B I Y Y
B R B E R Y Y Y N Y Y Y Y Y B B
R B R B Y C R R R B B B B B E Y Y
```

She had patience.

PICTURE SEQUENCE — PAGE 25

4	3	1
6	5	2

SIGN THE ANSWER — PAGE 27

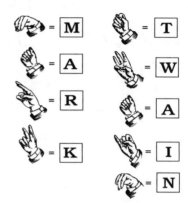

MARK TWAIN

NUMBER SEQUENCE — PAGE 28

6	8	10	12	14	16	**S**
10	15	20	25	30	35	**(C)**
3	6	9	12	15	18	**O**
50	55	60	65	70	75	**(H)**
75	80	85	90	95	100	**(A)**
22	24	26	28	30	32	**R**
25	30	35	40	45	50	**(T)**
8	12	16	20	24	28	**B**
5	10	15	20	25	30	**(E)**
10	20	30	40	50	60	**T**
20	25	30	35	40	45	**(E)**
65	70	75	80	85	90	**(R)**

T E A C H E R

MIX 'N' MATCH CODE — PAGE 31

"MY HEART
BEGAN TO SING!"

FOLLOW THE LINES — PAGE 32

PUMPING WATER

WATER

IN SHAPE WITH HISTORY — PAGE 33

" MISS SULLIVAN, YOU ARE FIRED!"

MYSTERY WORDS — PAGE 35

1. *Civil War*
2. *Alabama*
3. *Anne Sullivan*
4. *Laura Bridgman*
5. *hand*
6. *fever*
7. *doll*
8. *six*

L A R A B A A E L R D G M N H E E L X

Alexander Graham Bell

FILL IN THE BLANK — PAGE 36

1. Alabama
2. Anne Sullivan
3. sister
4. learn
5. spoon
6. alone
7. two
8. yes
9. signs
   hands
10. words
11. thirty
12. college
13. book
14. famous

LETTER SHUFFLE — PAGE 37

account	come	into	mince	on	to
acute	comma	it	mote	once	ton
am	commune	item	mount	one	tonic
an	cot	main	name	taco	tone
ant	count	man	neat	tame	tune
at	cut	mane	nice	tan	tunic
ate	cute	mat	nite	tea	unit
aunt	eat	mate	no	team	untie
came	emmit	mean	not	ten	
can	ice	meant	note	tie	
cane	immune	meat	nut	time	
cat	in	mice	oat	tin	

MATCHING GAME — PAGE 38

1. G		6. B
2. F		7. I
3. H		8. D
4. A		9. E
5. J		10. C

TRUE OR FALSE — PAGE 39

1. T	6. F	11. T
2. F	7. T	12. F
3. T	8. T	13. T
4. T	9. F	14. F
5. T	10. T	15. T

QUESTIONS — PAGE 41

1. *Helen Keller became deaf and blind when she was one-and-a-half years old.*
2. *Helen was very sick with a high fever that lasted for days.*
3. *Helen made motions with her hands to show what or who she wanted.*
4. *Helen's father was very kind to her, but he never disciplined her.*
5. *Helen became angry and frustrated because she could not communicate with anyone.*
6. *They went to the Perkins School for the Blind in Boston.*
7. *Anne Sullivan was sent to teach Helen.*
8. *The first word Anne spelled into Helen's hand was d-o-l-l.*
9. *Helen was so wild that Anne had to discipline her until she was tame enough to teach.*
10. *Helen always walked around the table, eating food from other people's plates with her fingers. Anne taught her to sit at the table and eat from her own plate with a fork.*
11. *Helen did not understand any of the words that Anne spelled to her. She thought it was a game.*
12. *W-a-t-e-r was the first word that Helen understood.*
13. *Helen graduated from Radcliffe College, wrote many books, and raised money for the American Foundation for the Blind.*

Certificate of Achievement

This certifies that _____ has mastered

Helen Keller

Total Learning Resource and Activity Book

From NEST ENTERTAINMENT, INC.,

by successfully completing all of the puzzles, games, and activities found herein.

_____
Nest Entertainment, Inc.

_____
As of this date